C000126031

Advance Statements
Workbook

The Rushcliffe Mental Health Support Group

Authors: Becky Shaw and Roger Smith

Advance Statements Workbook

Your Life, Your Decisions, Take Control

An easy to use step by step practical guide to making your advance decisions, preferences and directives

Authors

Becky Shaw and Roger Smith

Copyright © 2011

Covers designed by Becky Shaw

Cover photo by David Shaw

Artwork within book by Roger Smith and Becky Shaw

All rights reserved. No part of this publication may be reproduced, stored in a retrieval system or transmitted in any form or by any means electronic, mechanical, audio, visual or otherwise, without prior permission of the copyright owner. Nor can it be circulated in any form of binding or cover other than that in which it is published and without similar conditions including this condition being imposed on the subsequent purchaser.

ISBN: 978-0-9559591-2-7

Published by Becky Shaw

Becky Shaw
4 Holme Road
Bingham
Nottinghamshire
NG13 8DZ

With Many Thanks to the following people:

FUNDED BY

COMIC RELIEF

Comic Relief provided the initial funding for our pilot workshops to help people who had experienced extreme distress, learn about and create their own Advance Statement.

David Shaw's family have allowed us to use his photograph of Goliath Falls, Cornwall for the front cover. David passed away in November 2011 just a few weeks after taking this photograph.

The participants on the advance statements workshops held in Nottingham and Grantham.

All those who helped us with the preparation and editing of this workbook including: Anne Stone, Dr Martin Smith, Dr Keith Horsted, Terry Davies, Brenda Herzog, Jean, Charlotte and many at The Rushcliffe Mental Health Support Group.

Disclaimer

This workbook has been written with the best knowledge we have at the time of publication. It is always important to take into account any changes in the law and other legal requirements that may occur since the publication of this workbook. Although you do not need a solicitor to complete a legally valid advance directive we always suggest that if you are unsure you seek legal advice before completing any advance statement. Especially, if you have dependents that may be affected by your decisions you would be well advised to take legal advice.

Contents

Contents - continued

Very Briefly: What is an Advance Statement?

An Advance Statement is a statement of what you would like to happen or not happen if in the future you could be unable to look after yourself. It is for times when you lack capacity, which could be for reasons such as mental health difficulties, injury or dementia.

You may wish to think about what support you would want and what you would not want. You may also wish to include plans for looking after your pets, home, finances and anything else that may worry you.

This type of statement is useful for users of health services and, if agreed, their carers. It is likely to help health and social care workers with your care.

You may also have heard an advance statement described as a living will, advance directive, advance agreement or advance decision making.

Current Perceptions

When I showed the front of this book to a relative who works in an NHS hospital she said,

"Advance directives are a pain. We had a patient with one of those that said, 'If I am in a vegetative state, just let me die.' and 'do not resuscitate.' Fortunately he recovered and was discharged. We do our best to look after everyone, then you read this stuff and you think, 'What are we doing here?' I have never found these helpful."

The perceptions that all statements, '*are negative*' and '*to do with end of life*' are commonplace. Of course you can include preferences and directives about what you want to happen if you are close to death. This just is not an aspect that we have focused on in this workbook.

Advance statements are increasingly being used as part of wellness and crisis planning, where the objectives are staying well, what we can do to recover and how we and those around us cope when things are not going so well. The examples used on our courses and in this workbook are from these types of positive statements.

As well written advance statements become more commonplace the views of health workers seem to be changing as in this comment from a support worker, *"We find it so much easier working with people who have advance statements. You find out what is important to that person rather than forever trying to guess what it is they really want."*

Personal Reflection

Experiencing a mental health crisis is never good and getting the right care and support is essential especially at such a vulnerable time. I spent many years in and out of hospital and using mental health services. The support I received during these times was inadequate and detrimental to my health and wellbeing (physically and mentally). This lengthened the time it took me to recover from an acute crisis.

The poor support I received seems to have been due to some poor mental health services and some lack of understanding about what I needed during a period of crisis. Even though I had capacity to make many decisions about the help I needed I was not listened to or believed to have the capacity at those times. I therefore did not receive the support I wanted.

My parents would even express my wishes for me and they too were ignored. I was considered to be an adult and so my parents were not allowed to be involved even though I wanted this.

It was not until 2005 that I found out about advance statements. This has allowed me to say how I want and need to be supported in a period of mental health crisis. I knew I could end up in a crisis again even though I was doing everything I could to avoid one. I was so anxious about the possibility of having a future crisis because of the poor treatment and support I had received in the past that it was in turn making me ill.

Knowing my advance statement is in place, I feel confident that my needs will be met, my home will be cared for, bills paid and pets looked after and that I will be supported in the ways that help me to recover.

The first time I did an advance statement and needed to use it, for many reasons. This did not go as I had hoped. My wishes were not followed and I was not supported in the ways that I needed.

I was not clear about what I wanted and did not understand how to complete an advance statement in the best way and so my expressed needs could not be followed fully.

After doing a lot or research and rewriting my advance statement a second time and now a third I have learnt many things about how to make it more effective. During my most recent crisis and hospital admission my needs and wishes as expressed in my advance statement were followed. Being fully informed about how to complete an advance statement made this possible.

This workbook and the training are designed to help you learn about advance statements and if you want to make one how to complete it in the best way possible. We want you to have the best possible chance of your wishes being followed.

An advance statement is a useful tool when prepared in the right way and this workbook can help you. Hopefully you will never have a mental health crisis and never have the need to use the advance statement you prepare. I also hope that my advance statement does not have to be used in the future.

Becky Shaw October 2010

"I came to a workshop as a nursing student to learn more about advance statements because I may come across them in my work but I never thought I would go away and complete one the very next day. I have always known I should do a will in case I died but I had never thought about what happened if I lacked capacity. It's something you don't really want to think about. What would happen to my children though? Who would make decisions for me and would they know what I really wanted? I'd never thought about any of this before and now realise it is more important for me to do an advance statement than it is to do a will. I know what I would want and I would want my wishes to be met and this is one way of me doing just that."

"I have had a couple of mental health crisis in the past and I know from experience what treatments have helped me and I know definitely what hasn't helped. My wishes were not listened to at the time because I was deemed not to have capacity to make those decisions as I was too unwell. My family were not allowed to be involved even though I wanted them to be. I don't want this to happen again. My treatment made me worse rather than better. I now have an advance statement and this has taken the fear away of being forced to have certain treatments I don't want and it tells people supporting me what I do want. I know my family will be involved because I have expressly wished this in advance."

How to Use This Workbook

This book is going to be helpful to you whether you have had a mental health crisis or not. Once you have read this book you would not be alone in thinking that completing an advance decision is something that everyone should think about doing.

You may be interested in advance decision making because you work in the healthcare system supporting people with mental health distress, you may be a relative or a friend who helps to look after someone who has difficulties with their mental health or you may be interested for yourself in case you ever lack the capacity to make decisions (examples: mental health crisis, head injury or potential dementia). You will need to specify under which circumstances you would want the advance statement to be followed i.e. if you are having a mental health crisis or whether it is a head injury or dementia and whether the condition is long-term or short-term. Your wishes may be different for different circumstances. The basics are the same regardless.

This workbook can be used on its own or as a self-guided way of learning about advance statements and how to complete one. Alternatively it can be used to support training sessions. We have facilitated various workshops based on advance decision making, from two hour introductory sessions to one day workshops. If you or an organisation you work with is interested in a workshop please let us know. We can tailor the training to suit you anywhere in England or Wales. We know how beneficial this training can be to those who come and we want it to be accessible whenever we are able to do this.

Note: There are special rules now in place if you have a terminal illness and do not want resuscitation. These rules have been put in place to protect you and if this is what you are considering it is worth seeking specific advice. Your first port of call will be the health care professional responsible for your overall care (this could be a specialist at the hospital or your GP) and there are also many not for profit organisations who can help with this.

Looking Back

It is worth looking back to previous crises when deciding what could be helpful or not in any future crisis. We can learn a lot from looking back. This section is about reflecting on what has been helpful in the past and what was not.

We can consider a crisis to be any time when something or some things went wrong and you needed help to start making progress again. We need to think about what helped and what did not help. If you have difficulty thinking about the worst crises you have ever experienced you might find a less traumatic example that works in focusing the mind.

An accident might be an example. What led up to this accident? Were you flustered, over-worked or perhaps struggling to concentrate? Were other people taking risks? Did you receive help straight away? Was it the right help? Who was helping? What was done to lessen future risks?

If you are aiming to be prepared for a type of crisis you have never experienced before, consider if it is possible to talk with those who have had a crisis of that type or similar. There may be people in the health service or voluntary sector whom you can learn from. They may know about support and treatments.

Consider:

$\Rightarrow$ What has happened in the past in this crisis?

        o   What helped?

        o   What did not help?

Use the two grids on the following pages to reflect by writing down the areas that have helped or hindered.

We have split each page into four boxes. This will help you think about whether you were at home, in hospital, 'professionally supported' (meaning support from health services, your GP or any other types of support or care services). You may have been supported in some other way/from elsewhere. This is to help you think widely about what has helped or not helped. You do not have to use these boxes. Do it in a way that feels right for you.

What Helped?

At Home	In Hospital
From Services	**Other / From Elsewhere**

What Did Not Help?

At Home	In Hospital

From Services	Other / From Elsewhere

Crises do not just happen

This next section looks at what happens when we get stressed. If we can identify when we get stressed we can do something about it to de-stress. Thinking about and knowing what we can do to help us de-stress in advance can help us to do this more quickly and can help us with knowing what to include in our advance statement.

We all experience pressure and stress. We can all feel under too much pressure and we know that too much stress causes all sorts of health problems.

Understanding pressure and stress can help us avoid a crisis. First though, it is useful to know that pressure and stress are very different.

The Health and Safety Executive's definition of stress starts with:

"STRESS is the ADVERSE reaction

people have to EXCESSIVE pressure…"

From this we can see that pressure is not bad for us. It is only excessive pressure that is bad and that is because it causes stress. Pressure helps us lead productive lives. When we wake up in the morning we will normally start to feel some pressure to get out of bed. This is not bad. If we did not feel any pressure to get out of bed we might just stay there all day. Pressure, which can be defined as a force that compels us to do things, is so natural and with us almost all the time that many people, much of the time, are hardly aware of pressure.

It is only when pressure builds up that we begin to become increasingly aware of it. Often it is when we feel expected to be doing several things at once or to be in several places at the same time that we become acutely aware of pressure. Unrealistic expectations cause pressure. These may be coming from other people. Quite often a lot of pressure can come from ourselves, as we try to cram too much in. Maybe we are trying to please everyone? Maybe we are trying to get the most out of each day, as in the old expression, "Burning the candle at both ends."

Pressure is certainly nothing to be afraid of, just so long as we can have the right amount of pressure. Certainly we do not want too much, yet having no pressure at all would imply: no ambition, no expectations, no one depending on us… this would not be the way most of us would choose to live. Pressure is usually good, whilst stress tends to be bad.

What about stress?

By saying **"STRESS is the ADVERSE reaction…"** the Health and Safety Executive leave no doubt that the government's view is that all stress is bad.

This comes as a surprise for many people, who have heard expressions like, "good stress" and "a little stress does you good". These ideas are popular because we so easily mix up the ideas of pressure and stress. Any stress that seems to do you good is in fact pressure.

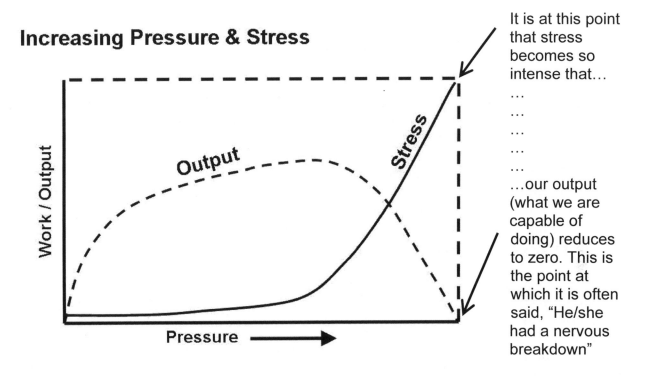

Increasing Pressure & Stress

It is at this point that stress becomes so intense that…

…

…

…

…

…

…our output (what we are capable of doing) reduces to zero. This is the point at which it is often said, "He/she had a nervous breakdown"

Stress is our internal reaction to excessive pressure that can damage our health. The fact that human beings tolerate and sometimes even seem to enjoy a few moments of extreme stress suggests that stressful moments do little damage. People can also live with low levels of stress going on for very long periods, without developing health problems that can be linked to this low level stress. The problems with stress happen when moderate (or more severe) stressors continue for too long or happen too often.

What causes crises?

Sometimes it seems as if a crisis can 'just happen'. We hear people say, "I suddenly became ill for no reason" and then on an insurance form someone wrote, "The tree just seemed to come from nowhere and caused the crash". Even if we do not know what caused our troubles there will still be a reason or more likely a lot of reasons that lead to an illness, an accident or any sort of crisis.

If we consider that anything bad that happens inside us can be called stress, we end up with several possible answers to the question of, 'What causes a crisis?'

- ° the same stresses going on and on
- ° many small stresses all adding up
- ° just a few big unexpected events/triggers
- ° one massive trigger

The bigger stressors, often referred to as triggers, are usually easy to recognise. These may include: a major accident, death of a spouse, being arrested, a wedding or divorced. All these involve a lot of stress that we feel at the time or immediately after the event.

The smaller stressors are usually less obvious. These can be relationship issues, such as noisy neighbours. Stressors can come from anything we consume, such as cigarette smoke, too much salt, too much saturated fat, alcohol, any foods we do not tolerate well, drugs/medications that cause damaging side effects. Poor sleep, lack of exercise and poor posture are sources of ongoing stress.

To demonstrate that prolonged stress causes damage and leads to crises a presenter can ask a volunteer to hold a small object at arm's length (arm horizontal/ with nothing to rest on).

The volunteer agrees the object is light and they have no problem keeping it held out for everyone to see. After a while the volunteer can no longer hold their arm out horizontally. The pain they start to experience is said to show how moderate stress gradually leads to health problems.

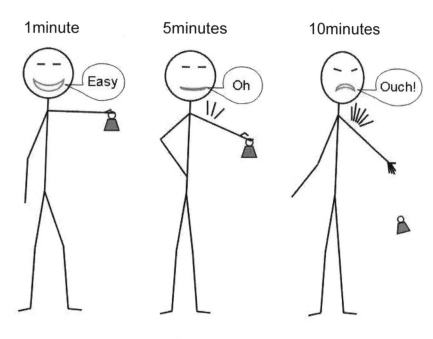

When there is neither a huge trigger nor a single prolonged stressor a third way in which a crisis can be brought on is simply with too many little stressors.

Is this like a waiter who easily carries a tray with just a few drinks, then as one by one more drinks are added begins to struggle with a risk of dropping the lot?

Is all stress bad?
The way stress is defined and the way we are talking about it, suggest that there is nothing good about stress at all. However, it is part of life. Trying to avoid every last bit of stress is not realistic and causes new problems.

For example:

Social phobia with fears of:

- any situation in which public scrutiny may be possible
- behaving in a way that is embarrassing or humiliating
- others thinking badly of them

Agoraphobia with avoidance of:

- particular situations because of a fear of a panic attack occurring
- places such as supermarkets
- driving for fear of a panic attack leaving home

Becky suffered from social phobia and chose not to go out much. After weeks of staying indoors and not meeting people, the idea of going out became increasingly terrifying. Certainly with social interactions, we need to experience a little stress quite often to keep up our resilience to everyday stressful events.

Thinking about the demonstration of holding a weight that represents stress, the healthiest thing to do is to pick up the weight from time to time to build up muscles, so that when you do have to hold the weight up it is a little easier.

Distress or De-stress
Excess stress eventually causes distress. Feelings of stress often alert us to the need to make lifestyle changes that can avoid crises.

In order to cope, and avoid a crisis caused by stress building up and causing distress, we can look at how we de-stress.

Looking Forward

Recognising Warning Signs of Excess Stress

Recognising warning signs can help you avoid a crisis point. It might be that you do not see the warning signs yourself and that it is friends, family and others close to you that notice them before you.

Recognising warning signs does not mean that you are going to have a crisis but it does mean that you can put support in place or increase coping strategies to help avoid a crisis.

An early warning sign

A later warning sign?

See page 29

What Are Your Warning Signs?

Warning signs can be physical signs, mental signs, or can appear as changes in your behaviour.

They will be many and varied and will be individual to you. The table below gives an idea of the types of warning signs that you may experience.

Are any of these warning signs for you?

Physical	Mental	Behaviours
Dry mouth	Anxiety/worry	More/less sleep
Trembling, Sweating	Anger	Indecision
Nausea, Tiredness	Poor concentration	Making mistakes
Muscle Tension	Fearfulness	Muscle twitches
Aches & Pains	Confused thinking	Eating more or Eating less
Headaches	Indecision	Argumentative
Indigestion	Negative thinking	Irrational
Palpitations	Gloomy thoughts	Doing too many things at once
Weight gain or loss		

"I tend to get agitated, anxious and do too much and end up sleeping too little. My friends tend to notice this before I do and start telling me that I should slow down and that I am doing too much. Once I recognise the signs I can do something about it. I make myself slow down even though I don't want to. I do more things to relax and take care of myself. It doesn't always work but I have avoided many crises by doing this."

What can I do if I am currently feeling too stressed?

One of the clearest indicators of stress levels is our breathing.

Paying attention to our breathing usually provides some quick relief. Stop what you are doing, listen to and feel your breathing. If you breathe a little more deeply and slow your breathing a little, symptoms of stress are likely to lessen.

Find help for understanding and developing your stress management - see resource 1 on page 91.

We all have a unique set of warning signs

On one of our courses Jane made this list of her warning signs

Physical	Emotions	What I tend to do
pain in gut	feeling rejected	wash less
nausea	feeling worthless	go out less
grinding teeth	less rational	not eat properly
acne gets worse	not caring about anything	avoid what I need to do
	indecision	rush
		make more mistakes
		miss appointments
		have accidents

You may have instinctively known when you have needed to take time out but you may not have always thought about the signs that have led you to know when this is. Think about your personal signs that you are becoming stressed / 'worn out' / 'run-down'.

On the next page there is a blank table for you to fill in any reactions to stress / warning signs that you recognise in yourself.

The column headings have been left blank as you may or may not think about warning signs as strictly 'physical', 'mental', 'behavioural' and may wish to add your own headings to your table. Note: Jane used 'emotional' rather than 'mental' as a heading.

If only a few come to mind now you can always come back later if you think of more that apply to you.

Some of my reactions to stress / my warning signs

It is important to heed our **earliest warning signs**; by the time we notice later warning signs it can difficult to avoid a crisis.

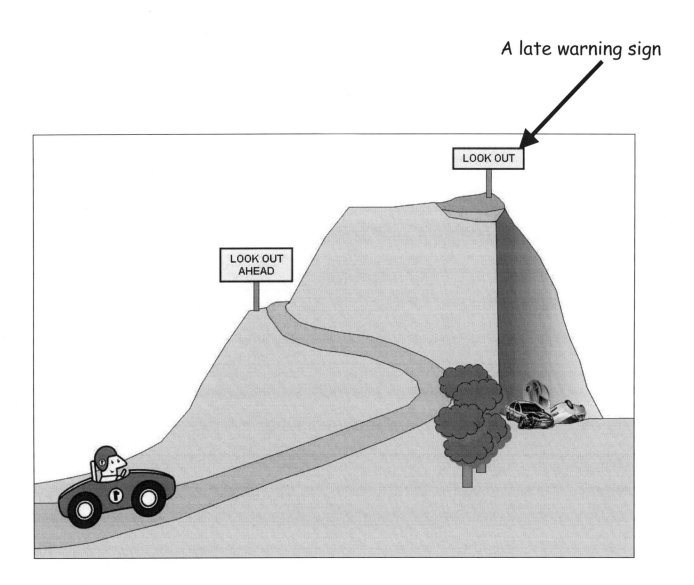

People who have been through many crises such as psychotic episodes or bouts of depression find that recognising and acting on the earliest warning signs helps them to avoid relapse.

Using the table you created on page 28, sort your warning signs according to when you notice them.

Some of my reactions to stress / my warning signs

The first warning sign I notice is:
Then I may notice:
Then I may notice:
Then I may notice:
Then I may notice:

What helps you avoid a crisis?

We all have many ways for de-stressing and we have different ways of describing these. Some people say that they relax, others say they unwind, others say they take time out. It can be difficult to think of all the things we do because they often come so naturally, like taking a bath or a walk or listening to the kind of music you like. Knowing what helps you de-stress can help you avoid crisis and help you recover more quickly.

Take a few moments now to write in this box some of the things you know help **you** to de-stress, relax or unwind.

When I need to de-stress / relax / recover / take time out

You may want to ask someone you know what they do to de-stress. This is useful as you may well find some new ways that help you to de-stress that you had not previously thought about. You may wish to add some of these when you do this next exercise.

Looking back at the earlier warning signs (you recorded on pages 28 and 30) see if you can match some of your de-stressing activities alongside these in this table.

Warning sign	One of my activities for reducing stress

Life's Cycle and Why it is Best to Plan for Future Crises

Wellness is rarely a steady thing. Some days we can be up and others we can be down. Some people feel good in the morning and others struggle to do much before noon.

We know that stressors affect these ups and downs. These can be little things that 'get on our nerves', like a car alarm going off, a misbehaving child, some small accident or the common cold. Whatever is stressing you, you will have more than just the list of your de-stressing activities that you can call on to stay well. In considering all the things that keep us well it turns out that we each have quite a tool box full of options.

Just as everyone has different stressors so everyone has a unique set of tools for staying well.

Some of the things I do to stay well are: to have breakfast every day, go out in the daylight whatever the weather, talk to a friend even if only on the phone or by email, have a shower to wake me up or a bath to calm me down.

Most of the time, our wellbeing tools allow us to stay in control of our lives and we maintain our 'capacity' to understand reasonably well what is going on and to make our own decisions.

However, when we come up against a stressor that is just too big or perhaps just too many little stressors we can start to become ill. If we become extremely ill we can lose capacity and so need others to look after us and many of the things that we would normally do until we are well again.

Good planning can include letting people you trust know about things that stress you and the sorts of warning signs they might see if you start to become ill. This can help in avoiding the sort of crisis where you lose 'capacity'. If people around you realise you are becoming ill and can help in some way crises can be avoided. For example: If going to a supermarket on a Saturday afternoon causes you to start panicking, you could explain this to the person you are shopping with and agree to go in the evening when it is much less busy. It is a simple example that illustrates that we do not have to tackle every problem head on. With understanding, a lot of stress can be avoided.

Wellness Tools and Crises

The idea of calling anything and everything we can do to stay well "Wellness Tools" has become commonplace for those recovering from crises. The phrase comes from Mary Ellen Copeland's Wellness Recovery Action Planning research and training (Resource 1 on page 91).

When teaching about wellness tools we have noticed that most trainees start off unaware of just how many things they are doing to stay well.

Wellness tools can be anything from setting an alarm clock, cleaning your teeth, walking the dog, listening to a particular radio show... There seems to be no limit to the wellness tools people can think of. Some, such as, 'getting outdoors when the weather is good' and 'drinking plenty of water', seem to be very common. Others such as, 'running 5 days a week' or 'being in bed by 9pm every night' would only work for a few people. What these examples show is that we all already have a unique set of wellness tools.

Stressful situations seem to lead to a crisis, although sometimes we seem to cope and avoid the crisis, whilst other times we do not. It is often using or not using our wellness tools that makes the difference. It is rare that we do not have the tools we need to cope. It is more often that we have forgotten about what keeps us well and helps us cope with stressors.

Example: Cynthia found walking to work and taking 30 minutes away from her work for lunch were important for her health. Following some bad weather she started driving to work and working through her lunch break, eating at her desk. These became habits. She stopped spending time outdoors on weekdays. When her father had a stroke and she was threatened with redundancy in the same week, she found she could not cope.

Wellness tools and Advance Statements

Wellness tools help us to cope with life's pressures and so reduce risks of crises. This reduces the risk of us losing capacity. It is good to have an advance statement - it is even better to never need to use it! Knowing and using your wellness tools may mean your advance statement can stay in place just in case it is needed, and never be needed.

Equally important is the likelihood that the preferences and any directives in your statement will originate from your wellness tools. You may well want to communicate what you know is good for you to those who one day may be caring for you.

Find help for understanding and developing your wellness tools (Resource 1 on page 91).

In this diagram the thickest arrow shows how a deep crisis can be avoided by planning ahead, using wellness tools and finding the right help.

Avoiding a crisis

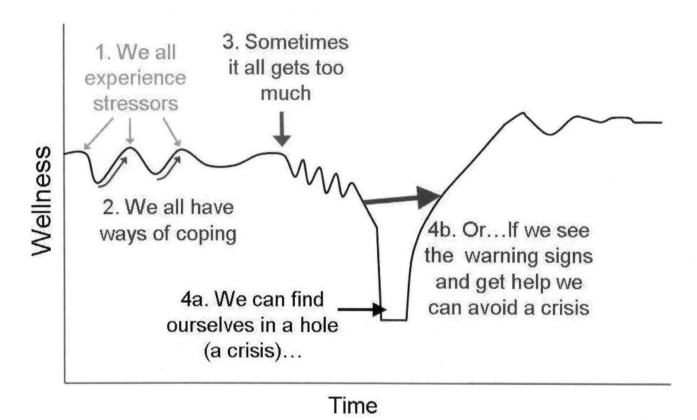

© 2009 Becky Shaw & Roger Smith

However much we plan, it is unlikely we will go through life without ever going through some sort of crisis at some time in the future.

Many of us will avoid repeating exactly the same crisis (*We can avoid falling down that same hole again*).

Unfortunately, different crises are out there and our best plans to avoid them may fail. (*We might fall down a different hole!*)

In this second diagram a crisis is shown as a dark pool of water. It is the sort of pool where help is needed to climb out. In both diagrams the far side of the crisis, (whether the hole or pool is bridged or not) is shown as higher. This represents how we can learn from crises and so no matter how dreadful our experiences of incapacity, we can learn. Learn from our mistakes and learn from adversity.

Thinking about these diagrams: the advance statement has two functions.

> ➤ One is clearly to make any crisis less painful.

> ➤ The other is that the process of making plans may help us to understand what we need to do differently to avoid future crisis. (Bridging the gap in the diagram.)

After a crisis

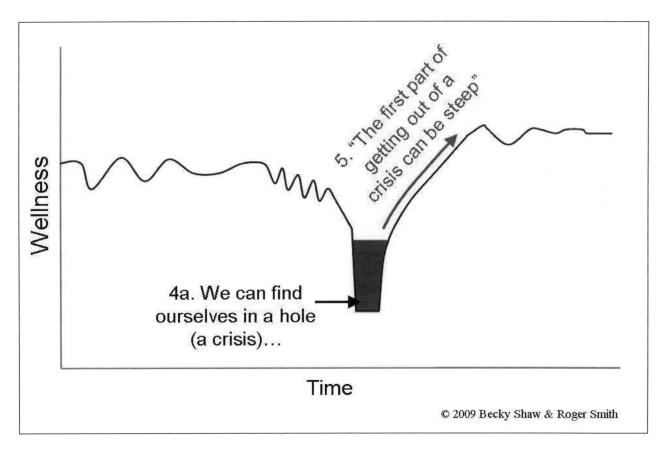

© 2009 Becky Shaw & Roger Smith

What is an Advance Statement?

An advance statement expresses what you would like when you are unwell.

It is written at a time when you are well and have capacity to understand what you want in case there is a time when you may lack capacity to make your own decisions. The advance statement is then used to inform what support you would like when unwell.

Your advance statement can be made up of two parts, your advance preferences and your advance directives.

Advance Statement

Advance Preference

➢ What you would like to happen

➢ Can be quite informal

➢ Agreeing what you need with others around you

Advance Directive

➢ It is what you are refusing

➢ It is formal

➢ It is a legal document

It is up to you to use the two parts in the way that best meets your needs.

We will look at what an advance preference is first before looking at what an advance directive is. There are some keys differences which we will outline for you and it is important that you understand the two parts of an advance statement. You may need to look back at this section to remind you.

Remember: Both parts need to be written at a time when you are well and are deemed to have capacity. It needs to be created independently, with a witness that you have done this while having capacity.

```
┌─────────────────────────────┐
│      Advance Statement       │
└─────────────────────────────┘
```

```
┌─────────────────────────────┐
│      Advance Preference      │
│                              │
│  ➤ What you would like to happen │
│  ➤ Can be quite informal     │
│  ➤ Agreeing what you need with │
│    others around you         │
└─────────────────────────────┘
```

An advance preference:

> ➤ allows you to record and communicate what you would want

> ➤ can include your wishes about almost anything

> ➤ allows you to say what you would like to happen

> ➤ it may be an informal agreement / it is not a legal document

Preference or agreement?

> ➤ It is your preferences that count. In making agreements about what you would like to happen you need to be sure the agreement really is what you want.

> ➤ You *can* write preferences into your statement without talking to the people concerned, *but* remember your wishes rely on good will. Talking with supporters tends to improve the chances of your wishes being followed. If writing, "Jack, please walk my dog if I am ill", it would be best to check with Jack that he could have time for this.

What goes in an advance preference?

> ➤ You choose ☺

> ➤ You can say what has been good for you in the past such as:
>> ➤ A particular medication, therapy, place to stay
>> ➤ Seeing a particular relative, friend, doctor or therapist

> ➤ You can say what was bad for you in the past

> ➤ You can suggest ways your friends may help you get what you need

Some limitations of the advance preference part of your statement:

> ➢ It is not a legal document. (The advance directive part is the legal part of your statement)

> ➢ It cannot contain directives (strict refusals). (These are in the advance directive part of your statement)

> ➢ Unfortunately it is no guarantee that what you want to happen will happen. People can choose to ignore your wishes in the preference part of your statement.

If people can ignore your preferences/wishes, why do we bother? Why not go straight onto the advance directive?

> ➢ Family and friends usually take a lot of notice of what you have said you want and need.

> ➢ Health professionals usually also take notice of your wishes. They know that their jobs are easier when they take notice of advance preferences.

> ➢ If you are creating an advance statement because of past difficulties then preferences can be a useful way of raising awareness of your needs and what would help you without having to use directives.

> ➢ Each of us who creates advance preferences raises awareness as we tell friends, family and health professionals about all the other ways that can help our mental health other than medication and hospitalisation.

Before we started writing this book we both assumed that professionals know all about advance statements. Talking with professionals as we researched the book, we found that most professionals knew very little and much of what was known was out of date. It is a good idea to explain as much as you can to family and friends, so they can then use it more effectively.

"The first time I needed my advance statement, healthcare staff knew it existed, but the staff still did what they felt was best. They went against my wishes. Unfortunately my children, even though they had a copy of my statement with them, did not believe they were allowed to challenge staff and suggest alternatives. My children, like me, assumed staff must understand about preferences and directives. Had my children felt able to speak up I think there is a good chance staff would have re-read my statement, my treatment would have been better and I would have been out of hospital more quickly."

```
┌─────────────────────────────────┐
│      Advance Statement          │
└─────────────────────────────────┘
```

```
┌─────────────────────────────────────┐
│          Advance Directive          │
│                                      │
│   ➤   It is what you are refusing    │
│   ➤   It is formal                   │
│   ➤   It is a legal document         │
└─────────────────────────────────────┘
```

An advance directive

- ➤ Allows you to refuse things that you are sure you would never want
- ➤ Allows you to say what you **do not** want to happen if you lack capacity to make your own decisions.
- ➤ If done correctly it will be a legal document that cannot easily be ignored.

Why is the word directive used?

- ➤ A Directive is simply a statement that you are refusing something
- ➤ It means something that you would not want if you ever lacked capacity.
- ➤ This is why we say that advance directives are all about what you do not want – your refusals.

Making an advance directive

> For a directive to work it has to be written in the right way.

> If it is not clear, professionals will not take any notice of it. This can be distressing both for you and for your relatives witnessing your wishes being ignored. This is one of the main reasons we have produced this workbook.

> If it is done correctly it can last for many years until you want to update it.

> It gives you choice and control over the things you know you would definitely not want to happen to you in a crisis

> Remember you cannot ask for something to happen (that would be an advance preference), you can only refuse it (health professionals have to respect what you do not want: it is a legal requirement).

> There are some limitations to what you can refuse to have and these are covered later on in the workbook

"The first time I wrote an advance directive I didn't write it in the right way. I knew what I did not want to happen if ever I was unwell again and I thought I had done it right. However I was not clear enough about what I did not want. My capacity at the time it was written was then questioned. My directives were not followed. It was upsetting. I have now made the directives in my new statement very clear indeed."

What Can I Write in my Advance Statement?

What can I write in the Advance Preference part of the statement?

Remember these are:

> ➢ Wishes

> ➢ What treatment / support I would like?

> ➢ Names of some of my supporters (with their permission)

This is where you say what you would like.

Examples:

> ➢ I would like my cats and dog to be looked after by my parents (or be taken to cattery/kennels).

> ➢ I would like to be supported by ********* and ******** (insert full names and say in what way). You may want to add contact details for supporters/other important contacts at the end of the advance statement.

Have a go at writing one advance preference.
Think about what one of your wishes might be.

What can I write in the Advance Directive part of the statement?

Remember:

> these are directives (refusals) about certain types of treatment

> directives (refusals) can be about many other things you do not want to be done

This is where you say what you do not want.

Examples:

> I do not want Electroconvulsive therapy (ECT).

> I do not want to be given ********* medication (insert full name of medication).

Have a go at writing one advance directive.
Think about one thing that you definitely would not want to happen.

Exercise A

Here is a mixture of advance preferences and advance directives.
Read the statement and put a tick in the "Preference" or the "Directive" box.

Note: One of these statements cannot be an advance directive or preference. Identify which one this is by crossing through both boxes and say why it can't be used as either.

Also: One of these statements is partly both an advance directive and preference. Identify which one of these statements is partly both by ticking both boxes and say why.

---

1) Jenny, Please be sure to let my mother know if I go into hospital and be as honest as possible about the circumstances. Thank you

Preference ☐   Directive ☐

---

2) When I have been sectioned in the past my father has hampered my recovery. DO NOT TELL MY FATHER, HENRY GEORGE COLE, THAT I AM IN HOSPITAL. This specific refusal to share information about me applies for all circumstances and for all hospitals.

Preference ☐   Directive ☐

---

3) If I have stopped taking medication I may be becoming unwell. If you cannot persuade me to start taking it again, try to get me into hospital without sectioning.

Preference ☐   Directive ☐

---

4) Haloperidol has made me feel suicidal – Offer me any medication but NOT Haloperidol.

Preference ☐   Directive ☐

5) In July 2007 I was taking the maximum recommended dose of Largactil* (active ingredient chlorpromazine hydrochloride). I went outside in the sun for just 10 minutes. The combination of the drug and the sunlight caused my face and arms to turn bright red and swell up causing pain. Susan Jenkins and John Fowler were present at the time and have photographs that can verify this event. This is why I refuse to take this drug unless it is deemed necessary to save my life and even then only if Susan Jenkins and John Fowler can be assured that I will not be exposed to any direct sunlight whilst on Largactil*/chlorpromazine.
(Note:
Chlorpromazine is for many people an effective tranquilizer. The above is a fictitious illustration and does not imply chlorpromazine has any more side effects than any other psychiatric drug.)

Preference ☐   Directive ☐

6) Zopiclone tablets give me a bad headache

Preference ☐   Directive ☐

7) If I get very high and start buying lots of things that I cannot afford and do not need, I would like my friend Susan to put my credit cards away in a safe place until I have agreed to take appropriate medication and she feels I am acting responsibly again.

Preference ☐   Directive ☐

8) If I am lacking capacity I would like my friend Martin to be informed 01884 312111.

Preference ☐   Directive ☐

9) When in hospital I found the most useful thing for my recovery was long walks. If I am not allowed to walk on my own please can staff walk with me? If staff cannot spare the time please try to arrange a timetable with Ian, David and Peter so that every day I have someone I can walk with.

Preference ☐   Directive ☐

10) The one drug I know of that I cannot tolerate is:

GENERIC NAME: carbamazepine

BRAND NAME: Tegretol, Tegretol XR , Equetro, Carbatrol

Even though I developed skin rashes in September 2001 and became extremely ill, an error was made and I was given this drug again on 23rd March 2006. The severe consequences have been documented in my medical notes.

I refuse to take any form of this drug under any circumstances. My father is one of the witnesses to this fact and he can be contacted on either 0116-326-0444 or 07763 121277.

Because of the serious nature of the reactions, should I be admitted to any hospital I want all the nursing staff to be aware of this, so that the kind of mistake made in 2006 cannot be repeated.

(Note:
Carbamazepine is for many people an effective mood stabilizer. The above is a fictitious illustration and does not imply Carbamazepine has any more side effects than any other psychiatric drug.)

Preference ☐   Directive ☐

You should have ticked 5 preference, 3 directive, 1 neither and 1 both.

You may now wish to check your answers in the appendix. If you have some wrong answers it will probably be worthwhile re-reading pages 39 to 43 to improve your understanding of the difference between advance preference and advance directive.

What We May Include

It is very important for advance directives to be worded in such a way that they are clear and unambiguous. This includes making sure that words are spelt correctly and the language used is clear and grammatically correct. There is a very good reason for this. If anything at all is unclear then one day someone may question how well you were at the time you wrote the directive and so question whether you had the capacity to make such decisions. Your wishes could then be less likely to be followed. It is equally important to spell drug names/treatments and the names of any individuals mentioned correctly.

For example 6 (from page 47) that currently cannot be used as either an advance directive or preference. Spend a few minutes seeing if you can reword it into an effective advance directive.

"Zopiclone tablets give me a bad headache"

Reword this sentence so you are not given Zopiclone

ADVANCE STATEMENT CHECKLIST

On the following pages are areas that you might want to consider when thinking about what to include in an advance statement. These are ideas participants on our courses and people we know have been thinking about.

We are putting these forward to give ideas of areas you might think about while you need to remember the choice of what to include is entirely up to you. There may be many other areas that you want to include in your advance statement either as an advance preference (what you would like) or as an advance directive (what you are refusing and do not want).

 **In Hospital**

- Name one or more medications you have found to be effective
- Any medication that does not agree with or suit me
- A list of other medications I am taking (dosages)

  (It is important to spell medication names correctly. A good tip is to copy the name directly from a previous prescription or ask your local pharmacist)

- Other things that would help me settle. Examples: own room, soft music, relaxation, quiet room etc.
- Sleep patterns
- Name of somebody who can bring in essentials
- Name of a carer to be involved in decisions about my care
- Someone you do not want involved in any of your care or not doing something specific.
  - Example: I do not want -------- looking after my finances
- Electroconvulsive therapy (ECT) - If you have strong feelings about this treatment it can be worth making these clear.
- Things that I enjoy doing / Things I do not enjoy doing
- People I hope will visit me/people I would like informing
- People I would rather not have as visitors. Some people say that they do not want to have any visitors - you should think hard before saying anything so drastic, as however busy a hospital may be, it can turn out to be a very lonely place indeed.
- Dietary requirements / Foods I enjoy even when I am unwell

At Home

o To look after my children… OR… Not to look after my children?

o 'Look in on' or maybe even look after my husband/wife/brother…

o Looking after valuables etc

o Checking the fridge for foods that maybe going out-of-date/off

o Appointments

- Is there someone you would like to check your diary, file-o-fax, any electronic diaries?

- Could there be appointments to be cancelled? Example: hair-dresser, dentist… This could be especially important if you are due to go somewhere where there is a charge for not turning up.

- Alternatively you may not want anyone looking in your diary and could state that people are "not to worry about cancelling anything as things usually work themselves out."

Pets

o Feeding - What, when, how much?

o When a cat should be let out/in, or perhaps when a cat should not be let out/in

o When a dog should be walked, maybe even *where* a dog should be walked/not walked

o To feed fish… and for non-fish keepers instructions about NOT overfeeding fish

 **Diet**

o   If you want a specific diet, how it is phrased makes a huge difference.

o   If requested a recognised diet that is based on religion has legally to be provided.

o   **<u>Vegetarian?</u>** There is no legal definition of a vegetarian diet, so *"I am a vegetarian"* can be read as a wish that does not have to be met. (Surprised? We were!) However: Writing, *"I do not eat meat, fish or poultry. Do not offer these as part of my diet"* creates a directive. When seen as a directive staff will be obliged to do all they can to ensure you are given the vegetarian options.

o   Animal derivatives are present in many products. Example: Lactose from milk is used in many tablets. It is possible to write a directive to refuse such products. (See Boxes 1 & 2)

Box 1: If the only essential medicines available all contain animal derivatives or have all been tested on animals even a well written directive can be overruled.

o   It is possible to refuse products that have been tested on animals. (See Boxes 1 & 2)

Box 2: Directives that cause staff to search for extra information, such as, "Were the ingredients tested on animals?" can delay treatment.

A directive could put undue pressure on the people trying to help you. A simple preference may be better.

Careful consideration of consequences is needed at the time of writing.

Work

- o If you are employed

    - What does your employer need to know?

    - Are there things you would rather your employer did not know?
      Example: Confusion or trouble could arise if an employer were to hear about a particular diagnosis. What if this diagnosis is only one of many possible reasons for you being unwell?

- o If self employed

    - What do your customers need to know about your absence?

    - What would you rather they did not know?

Mail

- o For security it is important that post is not left half-in and half-out of a letter box.

- o Are there particular letters or types of letters that you would like someone to open / and others you definitely do not want anyone to open?

- o Would you like some post brought to you and someone to help you go through it?

- o Or perhaps you strictly do not want to know about anything that might come through your letter box while you are unwell?

- o It can be good to make it clear whether gas, electric, water and other bills are paid automatically or not.

- o Credit card bills can be a particular problem.

- o Do newspapers need to be cancelled?

- o You may wish somebody to check your email for you.

Legal Issues

An advance preference is <u>not legally binding</u> on staff. However, if you have expressed what you would like to happen and what support you want and it is agreed in advance with those who would be providing your care it is more likely you will receive the support you need in the way that you need it.

An advance directive done in the right way <u>can be legally binding</u> on staff However, it is important to be aware of the legal requirements necessary for your advance directive to be followed.

The law requires

1. The circumstances specified in the refusal have occurred
   - The circumstances that trigger the use of the advance directive have to have occurred. (You are in the type of crisis you specified.) In the directive the circumstances in which you wish the directive to be followed need to be included, such as, mental health crisis, dementia, brain damage etc.

2. You were competent at the time of refusal
   - You need to be deemed as having been well enough to make a fully informed decision at the time when you made and signed your advance directive.

3. You have not been unduly influenced by anyone
   - It is important that you have not been influenced by anyone (or even if it could be questioned in the future that you could have been influenced by someone helping you even if they have not) when making your advance directive. This could be anyone; friends, family, mental health workers who might have persuaded you consciously or unconsciously to make a certain decision or change what you want. This is why getting someone who is independent to support you in writing your directive or in being a witness to your directive is essential.

4. You have understanding of the nature and effect of your decision
   - Those reading your directive(s) need to believe that you understood the consequences of the advance decisions that you have made. We will cover this in the next section.

5. Advance Directives must not contain
   - Refusal of basic care (See reference 8 on page 91)
   - Requesting doctors to act unlawfully or use treatment they believe is inappropriate

If you are sectioned under the mental health act 1983

If detained under the Mental Health Act 1983 you can have your refusal of a specific treatment overridden if the treatment is for a 'mental disorder'. Your statements should always be considered with respect by all mental heath professionals. In the Mental Health Act 2007 any written statement made when you had capacity needs to be considered. (Reference 3 Page 91)

There are currently action groups challenging the fact that if you are sectioned under the mental health act your advance wishes may be ignored. It is seen as a form of discrimination. These challenges may well change the situation in the near future.

If you are in a crisis but are deemed to still have capacity then you can revoke an advance directive or make one if needed.

Mental Health Capacity Act 2005

The mental health capacity act exists to help people make important decisions and to protect those who are unable to make an important decision (Reference 2 Page 91).

It is important to understand the basics of the mental health capacity act and how capacity is assessed. It is worth family and friends knowing too.

If you are deemed to **have capacity** to make a certain decision then your wishes will be followed. Your advance statement would not be necessary to use as you would be deemed to have capacity to speak for yourself for that particular wish/refusal.

You may be assessed as having capacity to make some decisions but at the same time, to lack capacity to make some other decisions. As soon as you are judged to lack capacity for any particular decision, your advance statement should be checked to see what you would want if you had capacity.

Who can assess your capacity to make a decision?
In general anyone can assess our capacity at any time. Many of us make informal assessments all the time as we try to keep our loved ones safe.

> Example: When June and Penny left the wine bar, Penny was opening the driver's door of her car, when June said, "I am not sure you are up to driving after two large glasses of wine. I am phoning for a taxi to get you home safely." Here June has judged Penny as lacking the ability to consider the consequences of driving whilst under the influence of alcohol. There is no suggestion by June that Penny is drunk, just that June knows Penny would never normally drink and drive. Knowing this about Penny she concludes that Penny is unable to weigh up the possible consequences at that moment.

We could have an advance statement that says, "If I have been drinking, whatever happens, do not let me drive. You know the trouble I got in last time I drove under the influence of alcohol."

The mental capacity act is mainly designed to regulate the more formal decisions made by professionals. One such professional is the Approved Mental Health Professional (AMHP) who is the professional most likely to be involved with 'sectioning'.

Basic principles (See resource 3 on page 91 for precise legal wording.)

➢ A person must be assumed to have capacity unless it is established that she/he lacks capacity.

➢ All practicable steps are to be taken to help the person make a decision before considering whether she/he is unable to make a decision.

➢ Unwise decisions do not indicate a person lacks capacity.

➢ Help must be given in the best interests of the person who lacks capacity.

➢ Help in a way that does not cause excessive restriction of the person's rights and freedom of action.

A person may be unable to make a decision for himself if he is unable to:

1. Understand the information* relevant to the decision

2. Retain that information long enough to make the decision*

3. Use or weigh that information* as part of the process of making the decision or

(*This information includes the reasonably foreseeable consequences of deciding one way or another, or failing to make the decision.)

4. Communicate his decision (by talking, using sign language or any other means)

A person is not to be regarded as unable to make a decision:

➢ unless the information has been given in an appropriate way (using simple language, visual aids or any other means)

➢ just because that person is only able to retain the relevant information for a short time

A lack of capacity must not be influenced by:

➢ age or appearance

➢ a condition (such as a previous diagnosis or disability)

➢ an aspect of behaviour / what you do

➢ previous difficulties/inabilities to make any decision

➢ difficulties you may be having in making other decisions in your life

So far as your advance statement is concerned be aware that the act instructs those who consider your capacity to consider:

➢ your past and present wishes and feelings (and, in particular, any relevant written statement made by you when you had capacity),

➢ the views of anyone named by you as someone to be consulted on the matter in question or on matters of that kind

The act also refers to the appointment of independent mental capacity advocates (IMCAs) and gives some information about what IMCAs do in relation to the mental capacity act. In general an IMCA can help ensure your capacity is judged as fairly as possible.

Capacity or not - case 1:

Liam has recently been so anxious that he is struggling to make decisions. When his brother asked if he wanted to go for a drink, Liam just kept saying, "I don't know. I don't know what to do." His father wanted to know whether he should go ahead and sell Liam's old bike. Again Liam said he didn't know and he couldn't decide. Even when his mother asked if he wanted three roast potatoes or four, Liam nearly burst into tears, saying, "It's all too much. I don't know anything."

Later that evening Liam told his family that he had decided to gradually take less of the medication and be medication free within a month. Family members believed Liam was not capable of making such a decision and if asked would have said he lacked capacity.

Would the Mental Capacity Act be in agreement with Liam's family about a lack of capacity?

Capacity or not - case 2:

Even with support from social services and a local charity, Mildred (95) has been unable to maintain the home her children grew up in. Her son is keen that she moves to a nursing home he took her to see six months ago and which she said she liked the look of. Mildred's daughter does not consider the nursing home to be suitable.

When they sit down together with a social worker, Mildred seems to remember the visit to the nursing home clearly. Her son explains to her why moving there will be good for her and she agrees with him. Then her daughter says why staying at home is going to be better and Mildred agrees with her. This goes on for some time.

When her son and daughter leave the room the social worker listens to Mildred and asks her some questions about the points put by her children. The social worker concludes that Mildred understands the question the moment it is asked but is failing to retain any of the information given to her about the advantages of each option.

Does Mildred lack capacity?

Nearest Relative

According to the Mental Health Act 1983 and 2007 your nearest relative is not necessarily your next of kin. Sometimes it is obvious who your nearest relative is, but sometimes it is not…

Do you know who yours is? Most people on the courses we ran did not know or assumed it was a particular person. They were shocked to find they were wrong.

Exercise B   (This had us scratching our heads.)

See if you can put these relatives in the order of nearness as described in the Mental Health Act. Put a '1' by the nearest relative, '2' by the next nearest and so on…

It can help to pretend that you have all these people in your life even though it is improbable all exist and are alive at this time.

Brother / Sister	
Grandchild	
Nephew or Niece	
Husband or Wife	
Civil Partner	
Mother / Father	
Grandparent	
Son / Daughter	
Uncle / Aunt	

Have a really good go at completing this before checking the answers.

Once you have completed the exercise check the answers on page 93 and 94.

Now you know the correct order of nearest relatives as defined in the law.

Check the list to see who your current nearest relative is in your life today.

Some people are surprised to find that it is not the person they automatically thought it would be.

If there is a dispute in your care and you lack capacity to make vital decisions it is the nearest relative together with the doctor who would have the final say. Knowing this can help inform what you include in your advance statement. It can also mean that you can act now to say in advance who you would like to have a say on your behalf and who you do not want to have a say.

Lasting Power of Attorney

This is simply a process for nominating someone who will make decisions on your behalf.

Power of Attorney

An ordinary power of attorney allows you to give authority for someone to act on your behalf. A typical example of this could be if a home owner has moved abroad and needs to give someone else the right to sell their home on their behalf.

An ordinary power of attorney will always cease if you lose capacity. A **special power of attorney** gives limited authority for someone to act on your behalf for specific reasons only. Again this power of attorney would be terminated if you ever lost capacity.

Lasting power of attorney (LPA)

A lasting power of attorney is different in that it enables you to say who you would want to make decisions on your behalf if you lacked capacity in the future. Just like an advance directive it can only be created at a time when you have capacity.

Example: "Mum and dad each have a lasting power of attorney so that if either of them ever had dementia I could then activate this power to make decisions on their behalf. They know I would have their best interests at heart and know what they would want."

Two types of lasting powers of attorney

The **Property and Financial Affairs LPA** allows you to choose a person you trust who would make decisions regarding how your money is used, managing your property and other financial affairs. You can put restrictions on their powers, such as, "You may not sell our family home." As with an advance statement clear precise wording is essential.

The other type is the **Health and Welfare LPA**. It again allows you to choose someone you trust who would make decisions on your behalf. These decisions would relate to all your personal healthcare and welfare. This may include decisions about consent for/refusal of treatment. It may include deciding where you live. Again you can put restrictions on this. This type of LPA is very useful if you do not wish your nearest relative to be making decisions for you. It allows you to choose someone you trust to have your best interests at heart and act how you would want. This person does not have to be related to you.

You can have both types of LPA or just one. A lasting power of attorney would only ever come into effect if you lost capacity to make decisions for yourself. As a precaution, in case the person you nominate may not be able to take on the role at the time you might lose capacity you can nominate a second power of attorney to make decisions with them or a substitute that will only make decisions if the first person nominated is unable to do so.

The person who is acting on your behalf under the power of attorney must by law always act in your best interest.

All types of power of attorney become valid only when registered with the Office of the Public Guardian.

An existing advance directive would still be valid but it is best to renew it so it is clear that it still reflects your current views, just in case any doubts arise.

Exactly like an advance statement your ability to have capacity to make certain decisions is made on each decision to be made. For example you may be able to make decisions about what to buy on a weekly basis but may be seen to lack capacity on bigger decisions like buying a new home or getting a loan. The person you have nominated to act on your behalf under the power of attorney would take your ability and capacity into account for each decision to be made (See Mental Health Capacity Act – pages 56 to 58).

You can create a power of attorney without a solicitor but problems can arise. It is best to seek legal advice especially if you have ever previously been seen to lack capacity.

It can be useful to have both an advance statement and a power of attorney as both will count and your power of attorney will then take the advance statement into account. Example: "My father's LPA will allow me to take care of his finances. His advance directive means his own choices of treatment and medication will be followed."

At the time of writing it is possible to access a BBC web page and video that includes information about costs for creating a power of attorney (See Resource 13 on page 91).

Doctor's certification of mental health capacity

Anyone can ask their doctor to certify they have the capacity to create their advance statement or lasting power of attorney.

If for any reason your mental health capacity could be questioned it is important to have a doctor assess your mental health capacity shortly before you complete your advance statement or create a lasting power of attorney.

Reasons for having your capacity certified include having previously had a mental health crisis, been seen to have lost capacity even if you do not feel you really did or if anyone believes you are losing your memory.

If you one day need to use your advance statement or power of attorney and your capacity at the time of creating these is questioned both could be overturned and not used.

When updating your advance statement a new doctor's certificate regarding your capacity may be needed. If you believe there could be any doubts at all then it is best to do get a new certificate as it is better to be safe than sorry.

Consequences

$\Longrightarrow$ **Consequences of what you put in an advance statement**

Imagine all the different scenarios you can for each of the advance preferences and directives you have made.

*"I ONLY WANT GEORGINA TO LOOK AFTER
MY TWO CHILDREN AND NO ONE ELSE"*

In an ideal world Georgina will be able to look after the children BUT what happens if Georgina can't? She might have gone on holiday or be unwell. If this is the case and you wanted no one else to look after your children social services might have no option but to make arrangements for their care. This could happen even if there is someone else who would be happy to look after them instead.

*"I DO NOT WANT TO BE ADMITTED TO
HOSPITAL UNDER ANY CIRCUMSTANCES"*

Hopefully you won't need to be admitted to hospital BUT what if you were seriously unwell physically? If this was the case then the doctors might say that this constitutes a refusal of basic care and that is not legal. Or if you needed an operation for a non-life threatening condition, while you are lacking capacity, you might not be admitted because of this advance directive. What if you were experiencing a serious mental health crisis and you were a danger to your self and others? The mental health professionals might then have no option but to section you under the Mental Health Act. Under section you would be taken to hospital with your directive over-ridden and quite possibly any other directives in your statement also being over-ridden. If you voluntarily went into hospital, no sectioning would be needed, and then the rest of your advance directives about what treatment and support you do not want would be followed. Medical professionals might also look at that advance statement and decide that as you were now in hospital they would not take much notice of anything else you had said.

Rewording your advance directives and preferences can make a big difference to whether they can or will be followed as you would ideally like. Both of the above examples of advance directives could be worded in a different way and other options given if needed.

In Exercise A you were asked to identify which statements were advance directives, preferences, both or neither. These were adapted from real life statements. Think about statement 2, below, from Exercise A and what problem may occur with this directive.

2) When I have been sectioned in the past my father has hampered my recovery. DO NOT TELL MY FATHER, HENRY GEORGE COLE, THAT I AM IN HOSPITAL. This specific refusal to share information about me applies for all circumstances and for all hospitals.

The person who wrote this may not have thought about all the different circumstances that may occur if ever they had to be admitted to hospital. They may be thinking about a mental health crisis and may not have thought about a physical illness or terminal illness. However it reads as though this person does not want their father informed of their hospital admission under any circumstances and this would be followed by healthcare professionals.

Directives are legally binding on members of staff, so you need to be sure these are written as clearly as possible and make efforts to eliminate all possibilities of misinterpretation.

Find someone to tell you what they think you mean by what you have written and spot any flaws or potential problems in the way it is expressed. You can then make the statements clearer as doing this will enable you to think about how others may interpret your wishes. Different people will read into what is written in different ways. It is essential that you are as clear as possible. It is also very common to think we have expressed ourselves clearly as we know what we want to say when in fact we have not.

$\Longrightarrow$ **Consequences of not having an advance statement**

It is worth thinking about the consequences if you do not have an advance statement in place and you become unwell and lack the capacity (or be *seen to* lack the capacity) to make decisions.

If you have been in hospital before you may know what it can be like to have no control or say over your care and what it feels like to be forced to have treatment and support that you do not want. You may have experienced treatment and poor support that seemed to make things worse or seem to slow your recovery.

If you have never been admitted to hospital it can be worth taking the time to think about what this might be like. Talking with people who have been admitted can help with understanding.

> ➢ What is important to you when you are unwell or if you became unwell?
> ➢ What support would you like?
> ➢ What treatment and support do you definitely not want?
> ➢ What would help you to recover more quickly?
> ➢ What would worry you? (Have another look at the check list on pages 50 to 54)

Having an advance statement can relieve these worries and give you more control over the support you receive.

Things to Remember

⟹   Capacity – are you well enough?

You need to have capacity at the time you complete your advance statement or it will not be followed or be a legal document. Your needs would not be met.

Capacity is the ability to understand the decisions you are making and the consequences of those decisions.

If you are admitted to hospital for mental health difficulties you might still have the capacity to make decisions, and understand what you want and need. You will probably understand the consequences of decisions too. However if a medical professional believes that you lack capacity it will not be a good time to create an advance statement. It is the same in the community when you are seen to lack capacity, (whether you do or not), any advance statement you create at that time is extremely unlikely to be followed. It is therefore important to think about whether you could be seen to have or lack capacity by others and also who will be the best person to testify that you have capacity.

By all means, plan your advance statement even if others think you lack capacity but wait until there is minimal or no doubt about your capacity before you create and sign the statement.

⟹   Who helps and who should not

It is also important that you are not unduly influenced by anyone when making advance preferences and directives. Again if you are unduly influenced by someone or are seen to have been - even if you have not - then your advance statement is less likely to be followed.

It is therefore important that you receive support from people who are not involved in your care when you are thinking about what you want to include and when you fill out your advance statement.

Close friends, family or mental health workers, although they will want to help, probably won't be the best people to help.

This does not mean that you cannot discuss later on what your advance statement includes but it does mean you have to be aware of the influence people involved in your care may have or be seen to have.

Writing Your Advance Statement

Have a go at writing a draft of an advance statement. It may be helpful to use the boxes you have filled out earlier in this workbook.

Making a start

It often seems that the most difficult part of any project is the first part - getting started! Surveys have revealed that millions of people say they are going to write a book "one day". When these same people are asked if they have made a start most have not yet written the first sentence.

If this book has inspired you to create an advance statement there is probably no better time than right now to create a draft version. It may be helpful to use the boxes you have filled out earlier in this workbook. You will have recorded; what helps you in times of crisis, and what doesn't help, your early warning signs and what helps you de-stress. These ideas can form the central part of your advance statement.

Some people find a blank page is useful to copy ideas onto, as this allows ideas to be grouped or put into some sort of order. You will need to consider if there something that is likely to happen first or that needs to be dealt with first.

If you are used to using a computer you may want to transfer your statements from this workbook to a computer file where you may rearrange these more easily.

If you feel strongly about certain things that you do or do not want but are unsure on other areas to include it may be good to do an advance statement which just includes those few things you are sure about rather than risk not creating one at all. It is easy to update and add or change things later but it would be distressing not to have your wishes met on something you were sure about.

Many people start by having a very short advance statement and then add to it over the years when they know more about their wishes. It is likely that you will not include all the things you have thought about in this workbook in your first advance statement although it can be very useful to keep a note of any ideas and thoughts for future advance statements.

It's not what you say. It's the way that you say it.

Think about your draft advance statement. Do any of your statements need to be reworded as advance directives refusing certain treatment or support?

If they are advance preferences, saying what you would like rather than what you are refusing, then they are not legally binding. If they can be re-worded as advance directives then they will be legally binding on staff.

At the end of this Workbook there is a blank advance statement for you to use. Not all the spaces have to be filled out. The spaces are there to help you think about all the different areas you might want to cover. You can leave areas blank. You can also have a very short advance directive stating just one or two things you do not want.

Being prepared to reword your draft statement to ensure grammar and spelling are correct. This can make all the difference between having your needs met and followed or just being ignored. If your capacity could be questioned in the future because of the way you have written it then your wishes may not be followed. Statements that are ambiguous may mean someone reading it is not sure what you would like. This will make it difficult for them to carry out your wishes. Once you have completed your statement ask someone you trust to read it and tell you what they think you would want. This will highlight any areas where you may need to be clearer.

Some people have their **advance statement written on a card** that they carry with them.

It can also be useful to carry a card to say that you have an advance statement in place and where a medical professional can get a copy if needed.

Remember: an advance statement can only be followed if the medical professionals and others who are involved know that it exists.

What should my statement look like?

Choosing a format and what needs to be included

There are many different types of blank forms (proformas) you can use. Some focus on mental health and others on physical health and some both. There are examples on the internet.

The one we have included focuses on mental health.

Use the type of advance statement that suits you and your circumstances.

If you are unsure you may be able to go to a solicitor for support (although this can cost a lot of money). There are other organisations that can help you and give advice. Some of these provide support free of charge or at a reduced cost. Age Concern and National Mind are just two places that may be able to assist.

Your advance directive can be as short as one line about one thing you don't want if you lack capacity.

For an advance directive to be legal it must:

> include a statement of intent (See pages 72 and 73)
>
> be witnessed (See pages 73, 75 and 81)
>
> be signed and dated
>
> be done when you have capacity on the date it was signed
>
> include the circumstances which have to occur before it can be used

Statement of intent

The statement of intent is necessary. It is needed to make it clear that you know what you are signing, why you are signing it and that you have the capacity to understand what you are signing and including.

You will need to explain in the statement of intent what circumstances would cause your statement to be used. People tend to state the circumstances they are most concerned about.

Example: "Both my father and grandfather suffered a stroke that left them lacking capacity. This is why I wrote, *'If I were to suffer a stroke or similar medical trauma'* in my statement of intent."

There again, there is no reason for not adding more possible circumstances and this could include: a mental health crisis, dementia, brain injury, unconsciousness because of an illness or unconsciousness through any kind of treatment, substance misuse.

It is certainly worth thinking for a few moments whether your advance statement is likely to be useful for a wide range of circumstances and the consequences if it is not.

Your advance statement may well be questioned: would you have wanted it to apply in a different circumstance from the one specified? There is a risk it may not be followed as you would have wanted if you lack capacity for a reason you have not specified.

This explains that you: have not been coerced by anyone, are doing this of your own free will, have capacity and understand your decisions and consequences.

This is where you specify circumstances in which your statement is to be followed. It can be changed to say dementia or for other physical illnesses or circumstances.

STATEMENT OF INTENT

Insert your full name in this space

I, ... being presently of <u>sound mind, willfully and voluntarily</u> execute this advance statement to ensure that, during periods of incapacity resulting from <u>psychiatric illness</u> my choices regarding my <u>mental health care</u> will be carried out despite my inability to make informed decisions on my own behalf. <u>I intend this document to take precedence over all other means of ascertaining my intent during periods of such incapacity.</u>

The type of care might not be mental health care so change this if needed.

This is saying you would like your statement to be the primary way your wishes are considered above anyone else's opinions such as family, friends, healthcare staff.

To the extent, if any, that this document would not be considered valid in law it is my desire that it be considered a statement of my wishes and that it be accorded the greatest possible legal weight and respect. I understand that this statement will become active and take effect upon my incapacity.

If you are under a section then the advance directives are no longer legally valid so this paragraph is saying if this occurred you would still like your directives to be taken into account.

The fact that there may be some incomplete sections or blanks in this document should not affect its validity in any way. I intend that all completed sections be followed.

This advance statement is valid from the date on which it is signed unless I decide to renew or dispose of it.

SIGNED: DATE:

I confirm that this form has been completed by the above named person.

First Witness - Name:

Address:

The statement is signed by yourself and your witnesses and is valid

This paragraph says that if there are blanks then this is deliberate and not because the statement is incomplete.

Signature: Date:

Second Witness - Name:

Address:

Your witnesses are signing to say it is really you who has signed that you are of sound mind, completing this statement of your own free will. They are **not** signing to say they agree with what your statement says.

Signature: Date:

A Sample Blank Copy of an Advance Statement:

ADVANCE STATEMENT

An Advance Statement is a statement of what you would like to happen or not happen in times of mental health difficulties/loss of capacity.

You may wish to think about what support you would want and what you would not want. You may also wish to include plans for looking after your pets, home, finances and anything else that may worry you.

This type of statement is useful for services users and, if agreed, their carers, and could help health workers with your care.

This document is the Advance statement for:

Name:

Address:

Date of birth:

Consultant:

Care Coordinator:

Carer (if agreed):

Date of Advance Statement:

It is my wish that at times of mental health difficulties this statement be given full consideration before, during and after my treatment.

PART 1: STATEMENT OF INTENT

I, ... being presently of sound mind, wilfully and voluntarily execute this advance statement to ensure that, during periods of incapacity resulting from psychiatric illness my choices regarding my mental health care will be carried out despite my inability to make informed decisions on my own behalf. I intend this document to take precedence over all other means of ascertaining my intent during periods of such incapacity.

To the extent, if any, that this document would not be considered valid in law it is my desire that it be considered a statement of my wishes and that it be accorded the greatest possible legal weight and respect. I understand that this statement will become active and take effect upon my incapacity.

The fact that there may be some incomplete sections or blanks in this document should not affect its validity in any way. I intend that all completed sections be followed.

This advance statement is valid from the date signed unless I decide to renew or dispose of it.

SIGNED

Date

I confirm that this form has been completed by the above named person

Witness 1   Name   _____

             Address   _____

                         _____

             Postcode   _____

             Signed   _____   Date _____

Witness 2   Name   _____

             Address   _____

                         _____

             Postcode   _____

             Signed   _____   Date _____

My Advance Directives are as follows:

If I am experiencing mental health difficulties **I do not want** the following to happen:

I do not wish to take the following medication:

My wishes are as follows:

I have found the following medication helpful:

If I am experiencing mental health difficulties I would like the following to happen:

In the past I have found the following helpful:

If I decide to stay at home I want the following to happen:

My wishes continued:

If I go into hospital I would like the following to happen:

I would like the following to happen regarding my home:

My finances

I would like my finances to be handled by: (Name of person/s)

I would trust this person to handle the following (delete as appropriate)

- look after credit cards and bank book
- cash benefits
- pay bills
- any other expenses

I do not want my finances handled by: (Name of person/s)

Other information I agree to share as necessary

NHS Number:

My Date of Birth:

My Current Address:

THE FOLLOWING NAMED PEOPLE, WHERE POSSIBLE, AGREE TO CARRY OUT MY WISHES AS STATED ABOVE

I agree to the following contact details being shared as needed

Care Coordinator:

Next of Kin:

Solicitor:

Advocate:

Social Worker:

Community Psychiatric Nurse:

General Practitioner:

Day Centre Key worker

Relatives to be informed:

Relatives not to be informed:

Friends to be informed:

Other people not to be informed:

I agree to the following people having a copy of my advance statement

Name   Name

Address   Address

Advance Statement Miniaturised

An A5 version could be folded to go in a diary, wallet or handbag

ADVANCE STATEMENT FOR:

ADVANCE DIRECTIVES – This is what I want to refuse:

If I am experiencing mental health difficulties **I do not want** the following to happen: _____

_____

_____

I do not wish to take the following medication: _____

_____

THE FOLLOWING PEOPLE AGREE TO HELP ENSURE MY WISHES ARE CARRIED OUT

I agree to the following contact details being shared as needed

Care Coordinator:

Next of Kin:

Solicitor:

Advocate:

Social Worker:

Psychiatric Nurse:

GP:

Relatives to be informed:

Relatives not to be informed:

Friends to be informed:

Other people not to be informed:

I agree to the following people having a copy of my advanced statement

Name _____

Address _____

Name _____

Address _____

ADVANCE STATEMENT FOR:

Name: _____

Address: _____

Date of birth: _____

Consultant: _____

Date of Advance Statement: _____

It is my wish that at times of mental health difficulties that this statement is given full consideration before, during and after my treatment.

STATEMENT OF INTENT

I, _____ being presently of sound mind, wilfully and voluntarily execute this advance statement to ensure that, during periods of incapacity resulting from psychiatric illness my choices regarding my mental health care will be carried out despite my inability to make informed decisions on my own behalf. I intend this document to take precedence over all other means of ascertaining my intent during periods of such incapacity.

To the extent, if any, that this document would not be considered valid in law, it is my desire that it be considered a statement of my wishes and that it be accorded the greatest possible legal weight and respect. I understand that this statement will become active and take effect upon my incapacity.

The fact that there may be some incomplete sections or blanks in this document, should not affect its validity in any way. I intend that all completed sections be followed.

This advance statement is valid from the date on which it is signed unless I decide to renew or dispose of it.

SIGNED _____ Date _____

I confirm that this form has been completed by the above named person

Witness 1 – Name _____

Address _____

Postcode _____

Signed _____ **Date** _____

Witness 2 – Name _____

Address _____

Postcode _____

Signed _____ **Date** _____

Witnesses

The witnesses are needed to sign the form to show that you did have capacity at the time to understand what you were signing, that you have signed the document of your own free will and that it is indeed you that had signed and not someone else.

The witnesses are **not** signing the form to say they agree with what you have put. They are only signing to say that you have the capacity to make your own decisions at that time.

Who you choose as your witnesses can influence whether the advance directives are followed or not. If it is ever suggested that one of your witnesses influenced your statement then its validity could be questioned. Close friends, family members and mental health workers are more likely to be seen to have influenced you, than people who seem to be less associated with your personal life.

It is best to get someone to witness your advance directive who is independent of your care and who can say that you have capacity to make that decision meaning you are well enough at the time. Vicars, solicitors and teachers are often asked to witness documents.

An advance directive can be given orally. In general oral advance directives are less likely to be followed as health professionals will not necessarily see them and will only know about them if they talk to someone who heard the directive. An oral advance directive is more likely to have its validity questioned. A doctor would usually write any oral advance directive down in your medical notes although access to these notes is restricted and might not be seen by those treating or supporting you when it is needed.

Remember: there are many different types of blank forms you can use but whatever form you use you can fill in part or all of it depending on what you want and need to use it for.

Reflecting before signing and storing

By now you will probably know whether completing an advance statement is right for you. You may have decided on what you want and may even have created your statement.

It is important that before you and your witnesses sign that you take time to reflect on your decisions, the impact they will have and the way you have worded them. Perhaps share what you have decided with friends, family, mental health workers or other people using the mental heath services so that they can comment on what you have said and the way that you have said it.

Ask yourself;

⟹ When they read my advance statement do they know what I want?

⟹ Is it practical?

⟹ Will they have time to do what I ask?

⟹ Are their circumstances likely to change over the next few months or years

⟹ Are any of my supporters planning to move house?

⟹ Do I need to reword anything or add any clarification?

⟹ Have I forgotten anything?

Reflecting is essential and there will be probably be some changes or additions that you want to make.

Where to keep copies of your Advance Statement

People need to know you have an Advance Statement and know where to find it. Here is a business card idea, simply stating that you have a directive and where copies are kept.

This card confirms that I have an Advance Statement.

Name: Jo Bloggs

Signed……………… Date ……………..

Copies of my Advance Statement are with:

> **My Brother - Tim Bloggs   07895 777477**
>
> **And**
>
> **My GP - Dr Simon Hill   01522 454545**

Copies

You can make as many copies as you want. Keep a list of who has a copy so that if you update it in the future they all receive an updated copy and are asked to destroy the one they have if you no longer want to use it.

Who needs to see it or have a copy?

- ➢ You choose
- ➢ Probably everyone who is mentioned in the statement
- ➢ Probably every relative and friend who is likely to be involved with your treatment
- ➢ Key health professionals such as your GP

Updating each copy and letting people know
– Why is this essential?

It is especially important to update your advance statement if your circumstances have changed.

It is important to date every copy of the advance statement that you make. The most recent copy will make the earlier copies redundant.

Even if your circumstances do not change much or even if nothing changes for you at all for years you will still need to update your advance statement from time to time. An advance statement that is five or more years old could be said to be too old to be able to reflect your wishes in the present day.

Tell people you have an advance statement. There is no point in having one if people do not know it exists. It cannot be followed if the people who are going to be treating and supporting you in a time of crisis do not know about it.

Family and friends who have a copy can use it as a tool to get you the support you need when you need it. Letting family members have a copy that they can produce when needed can help make sure that the right people are supporting you in a time of crisis. Family can tell staff about both the existence and content of your advance statement.

There is a balance to be achieved between ensuring there are copies in the right places/with the right people whilst not having so many copies that it becomes too difficult to keep track of these and be certain they are all up to date.

One approach is to ensure at least one family member and at least one health professional has a copy. Really though it is very much your choice. Whom you decide to give copies to will depend on your circumstances, perhaps past experiences and the sorts of crisis that are covered by your advance statement.

Exercise C

Test what you have learnt with this exercise.

Fill in the rest of the words, a dash indicates a letter is missing and to help you we have included some of the letters in the missing words. Answers are in the appendix.

1.   An advance statement is made up of two parts,
      __ D __ __ __ __ __   P __ __ __ __ __ __ __ __ __
      and __ __ __ __ __ __ __ D   __ __ R __ __ __ __ __ __.

2.   An advance directive is to say what you do __ __ T want. It is also known as an advance R __ __ __ __ __ __ .

3.   An advance __ R __ __ __ __ __ __ __ __ E says what support you would like.

4.   An advance statement is written at a time when you are __ __ L __ and have __ __ P __ __ __ __ Y.

5.   In an advance statement you say what you would like to happen and what you do not want to happen in case of any future __ R __ __ __ __ .

6.   An advance statement needs to be S__ __ __ __ D, __ A __ __ D and __ __ T __ __ __ __ __ D and contain a statement of __ N __ __ __ T.

86

7. You can not ask a doctor to act U __ L __ __ __ __ __ __ __.

8. You can not refuse __ A __ __ C __ A __ __.

9. An advance __ __ __ __ __ __ __ __ __ can be legally binding if written in the right way.

10. An advance __ __ __ __ __ __ __ __ __ __ __ is not legally binding but your wishes should be considered and followed where possible by medical staff when making clinical decisions.

11. An advance directive can be __ V __ R __ __ __ __ __ N if you are sectioned under the mental health act 1983.

12. I can keep copies of my advance statement with __ N __ __ __ __ I choose.

13. I can __ P __ __ __ __ my advance statement at __ __ Y __ __ __ __ and this makes any previous advance statement obsolete.

Reflecting on when is the right time to make an advance statement

Most of us realise how useful it will be for our relatives if we make a will, then we put it off for years. It does not seem to be a priority.

It was a chance meeting with an expert in will writing that inspired me to make a will.

The similarity with advance statements is clear. It rarely seems to be a priority and it is so easy to put off for another day. I have been judged to lack capacity and have been given the wrong treatments and treated against my will yet, I have found it easy to think of excuses for not having an advance statement. "Oh, they won't take any notice.", "Who would I give a copy to?" or "Nobody would want to keep a copy for me."

It now seems extraordinary that it was only months into this project with Becky that all of these excuses started to look rather silly. Even then, it was only when I thought about the similarity to a will that I realised that creating a simple advance directive is not so hard and I would feel better for completing it.

Following the exercises Becky and I had designed a few years earlier helped me to realise the worries in my mind about medications and ECT were now not so relevant for me. These days, I wonder who will pay the bills, let my clients know I am not available and I have a very modern worry of no one else knows passwords to my bank accounts, social networking and so on. My advance statement is not typical, but then no two advance statements are ever going to be the same.

We are all unique and our wishes will be unique.

Roger Smith August 2011

Contents for Appendices

References, resources, and useful contacts

Avoiding illness/avoiding loss of capacity

1. For understanding and developing wellness tools see Wellness Recovery Action Planning at www.copelandcenter.com or www.wraptraining.co.uk

The law

2. The Mental Capacity Act 2005 www.legislation.gov.uk/ukpga/2005/9/contents

3. The Mental Health Act 2007 www.legislation.gov.uk/ukpga/2007/12/contents

4. Jones R (2010) *The Mental Health Act Manual (13th edition)* Sweet and Maxwell. Includes reference to the 'Code of Practice - Mental Health Act 1983'

5. Brown R, Barber P, Martin D (2005) *The Mental Capacity Act 2005: A Guide for Practice (Post-Qualifying Social Work Practice)*

6. Care Quality Commission (Oct 2010) *Monitoring the use of the Mental Health Act*
   http://www.cqc.org.uk/mentalhealthactannualreport2009-10.cfm
   "…in 2009/10 there were 45,755 detentions under the Mental Health Act in the year 2009/10"

7. The mental health charity, Mind can be a good source of easy to read legal information:
   http://www.mind.org.uk/help/rights_and_legislation

Dementia

8. Alzheimer's Society's factsheet on Advance Decisions:
   http://www.alzheimers.org.uk/site/scripts/documents_info.php?documentID=143

Making a will / Power of Attorney

9. Will: www.direct.gov.uk/en/Governmentcitizensandrights/Death/Preparation/DG_10029800

10. Lasting Power of Attorney in England and Wales -
    Short cut to overview: www.direct.gov.uk: http://tinyurl.com/5vfbhtl
    Forms for completion: www.justice.gov.uk/global/forms/opg/lasting-power-of-attorney/index.htm

11. Lasting Power of Attorney in Scotland: www.publicguardian-scotland.gov.uk

12. Northern Ireland and The Office of Care and Protection: www.courtsni.gov.uk

13. BBC: www.bbc.co.uk/blogs/theoneshow/2010/01/power-of-attorney-top-tips.shtml

More detailed reading

14. Atkinson J. (2007) Advance Directives in Mental Health; Theory, Practice and Ethics. London, Jessica Kingsley Publishers (Especially page 58 where English and Scottish law is compared)

Answers to Exercise A (Page 46 to 48)

1	Preference
2	Directive
3	Preference
4	Directive
5	Preference and Directive Note: This could confuse a medical professional treating you.
6	Neither. It is just stating a fact. "Zopiclone gives me a bad headache". It does not say what you would like or whether you are refusing to take it or not. A medical professional could interpret this in many different ways.
7	Preference
8	Preference
9	Preference
10	Directive

Answers to Exercise B (Page 59)

Nearest Relative

Here are the official answers according to the Mental Health Act 1983/2007.

Brother / Sister	4
Grandchild	6
Nephew or Niece	8
Husband or Wife	1=
Civil Partner	1=
Mother / Father	3
Grandparent	5
Son / Daughter	2
Uncle / Aunt	7

Note: With the introduction of the Mental Health Act 2007, adults living together 'as husband and wife', civil partners and same sex partners are all considered equal with married couples, providing they/you have been living together for at least 6 months.

Putting these in order:

Husband or Wife	1=
Civil Partner	1=
Son / Daughter	2
Mother / Father	3
Brother / Sister	4
Grandparent	5
Grandchild	6
Uncle / Aunt	7
Nephew or Niece	8

For most of us this list will be all that is needed to be sure who our nearest relative is. If you live with your husband then it is your husband. If you have never been married, have no civil partner, no children, and your mother or father is alive then your nearest relative is your mother or father.

It can be more complex and there are additional rules that cover many other possibilities:

➤ If you have two relatives who appear to be equal on the list, such as a brother and a sister, the older one is considered to be the nearer relative. However if the younger one lives with you and the older one does not then the younger one could be the nearer relative. This will depend on how long they have lived with you. If you need to be sure it is worth reading some of 'The Mental Health Act Manual' (See reference 4 on Page 97)

➤ Relatives of half blood may be treated the same as those of whole blood ("for purposes of sectioning")

➤ A person who is not a relative but who has been living with the person concerned for at least five years can also be considered as Nearest Relative.

In some rare circumstances it can be necessary to seek legal advice to clarify who is your Nearest Relative.

Answers Exercise C (Pages 86 & 87)

1. An advance statement is made up of two parts, an <u>ADVANCE</u> <u>PREFERENCE</u> and an <u>ADVANCE</u> <u>DIRECTIVE</u>.

2. An advance directive is to say what you do <u>NOT</u> want. It is also known as an advance <u>REFUSAL</u>.

3. An advance <u>PREFERENCE</u> says what support you would like.

4. An advance statement is written at a time when you are <u>WELL</u> and have <u>CAPACITY</u>.

5. In an advance statement you say what you would like to happen and what you do not want to happen in case of any future <u>CRISIS</u>.

6. An advance statement needs to be <u>SIGNED</u>, <u>DATED</u> and <u>WITNESSED</u> and contain a statement of <u>INTENT</u>.

7. You can not ask a doctor to act <u>UNLAWFULLY</u>.

8. You can not refuse <u>BASIC</u> <u>CARE</u>.

9. An advance <u>DIRECTIVE</u> can be legally binding if written in the right way.

10. An advance <u>PREFERENCE</u> is not legally binding but your wishes made should be considered and followed where possible by medical staff when making clinical decisions.

11. An advance directive can be <u>OVERRIDDEN</u> if you are sectioned under the mental health act 1983.

12. I can keep copies of my advance statement with <u>ANYONE</u> I choose.

13. I can <u>UPDATE</u> my advance statement at <u>ANY</u> <u>TIME</u> and this makes any previous advance statement obsolete.

Answers to case studies regarding capacity (Page 58)

Case 1 Answer:

Liam is struggling with making choices. However, there is nothing in the example that suggests he cannot make his own mind up about medication. It could be that with some rest he could make some decisions. It may be that too many choices at once is causing him to struggle or that his mental health might fluctuate throughout the day enabling him to make decisions some times and not at other times. In the Mental Capacity Act it is the capacity to make individual decisions that matters. There may be hundreds of things that Liam cannot decide about but these cannot on their own be used to judge him to lack capacity in everything.

Liam could be asked further questions (either by a family member or a mental health advocate) to clarify whether he lacked capacity to make this particular decision or not such as asking why do you want to reduce your medication? This would be to ascertain whether he fully understood the consequences of doing this and his reasons. It would not be right for us to judge whether it would be right for Liam or not to reduce his medication only to assess whether he had the capacity to make that decision.

While we have capacity we all have the right to make a decision for ourselves even if others feel those decisions maybe unwise.

Capacity 2 Answer:

Of course we cannot judge anyone's capacity based on such a short description, however, there is reason to suspect Mildred is lacking capacity, in that she seems to have problems with her short term memory. The Mental Capacity Act says that a person needs to not only understand the information but also retain it for long enough to be able to make the decision. It is a difficult decision and professionals with a good understanding of the act ('best interest assessors') could be asked to help.

Mildred might also need some support in being able to understand the question she is being asked and there may be ways of helping her. Good support and accessible clear information is needed before it can be assessed whether she lacks capacity or not. A different way of providing the information on the choices, such as revisiting the nursing home, may well mean she then can make an informed decision.

Health Professional Titles and Changes in Roles Since 2007

Approved Mental Health Professional (AMHP) is a role similar to the approved social worker replaced by the Mental Health Act 2007. The AMHP duties include coordinating mental health assessments and section decisions.

[Consider how you will ensure that your advance statement will be seen by this person or the RC if they were to assess you.
Example: you could ask your mental health care coordinator to keep it with your crisis plan/care plan or highlight that you have one and were it is kept]

Independent Mental Health Advocate (IMHA) – The Mental Health Act 2007 created this advocate role. If you qualify for IMHA assistance they will visit you, listen to you and help you obtain information.
[If you are likely to receive treatment for MH issues you may well qualify for assistance from an IMHA]

Independent Mental Capacity Advocate (IMCA) – Often referred to as an 'IMCA'. This professional will only come to your assistance if you have no family and friends to support you. If you have no other support an IMCA is likely to be involved in the most serious decisions. An IMCA is not a decision maker, but the decision maker will have a duty to take into account the information given by the IMCA.

Responsible Clinician (RC): They have a role similar to the Responsible Medical Officers replaced by the Mental Health Act 2007. The RC is in overall charge of patients in hospital under section.

Some ideas of actions you could take if you have been judged to lack capacity and you believe you still have capacity?
1. Raise the matter with the person (the AMHP?) who conducted the assessment.
2. Ask for a second opinion.
3. Consider using:
    a. The local complaints procedure
    b. Mediation
    c. A case conference.
4. Complain to the Public Guardian.
5. Apply to the Court of Protection.
6. Seek guidance for resolving disagreements from the Mental Capacity Act 2005 code of Practice.

Definitions

Advance Agreement is the same as an advance preference. The term may be used where you feel sure anyone mentioned in your preference statement agrees with what you are asking of them.

Advance Preference is a type of statement that is not legally binding.

Advance Statement is a statement of what you would like to happen or not happen in times of mental health difficulties/loss of capacity.

> Advance Decision: This is exactly the same as an Advance Directive and is always about what you do not want to happen should you lose capacity.

Attorney: This simply means 'agent' which of course means someone who acts on your behalf.

> Enduring Power of Attorney: These are historical documents since the introduction of the Mental Capacity Act 2005 and the introduction of Lasting Power of Attorney. Old EPAs continue to be valid if registered with the Office of the Public Guardian.

> Power of Attorney: An authorization for someone to act as your agent. These are often used for financial matters when an agent is asked to look after bank accounts, pay bills and so on.

> Lasting Power of Attorney (LPA): A legal document that lets you appoint someone you trust as an 'attorney' to make decisions on your behalf. It has no legal standing until it is registered with the Office of the Public Guardian. A registered LPA can be used at any time, whether you have the mental capacity to act for yourself or not. Unlike an Advance Directive an LPA can be used when you have capacity as well as when you lack capacity.

Best interests: The Mental Capacity Act 2005 says that professionals must make decisions in your best interests. Guidance to them includes that they should consider:

> Any written instructions (such as Advance Statements)

> Advance Decisions

> Cultural Norms

> The opinions of carers and others who know you

Capacity: Having mental capacity means a person can make their own decisions.

DoL = Deprivation of Liberty: Health professionals often use the expression 'DoL', which is about hospital patients who may need to be detained for an extended time. The Mental Health Act 2007 gives six requirements that have to be met before a patient can be deprived of their liberty. [Note: The sixth of these requirements is there is: No valid Advance Directive refusing this type of care.]

Living Will
Living will is simply an alternative description of an advance statement.

The Mental Capacity Act 2005:
> Lists 4 ways in which a person may be judged to lack capacity
> Suggests 6 causes for loss of capacity
> Says how capacity can be assessed – always starting by assuming the person has capacity
> Says when capacity should be assessed
> And who should be involved with assessing capacity
> Guidance on how assessments can be made

Mental Health Act 1983: This still exists but much of it has been superceded by the Mental Health Act 2007.

Mental Health Act 2007: This came into law during 2008 and is now the main law governing mental health matters.

Nearest Relative: This is discussed in this workbook on pages 59, 60, 93 and 94.

Next of kin: This might seem like an important idea but it means little in mental health law, where the nearest relative is a far more important factor.

Blank advance statement

You may wish to use the dashed vertical line on the left to cut out these pages or simply photocopy and use,

You may wish to adapt it as needed
(Pages 101 through to 107)

ADVANCE STATEMENT

An Advance Statement is a statement of what you would like to happen or not happen in times of mental health difficulties/loss of capacity.

You may wish to think about what support you would want and what you would not want.

You may also wish to include plans for looking after your pets, home, finances and anything else that may worry you.

This type of statement is useful for services users and, if agreed, their carers, and could help health workers with your care.

This document is the Advance statement for:

Name:

Address:

Date of birth:

Consultant:

Care Coordinator:

Supporter/Carer (if agreed):

Date of Advance Statement:

It is my wish that at times of mental health difficulties that this statement is given full consideration before, during and after my treatment.

PART 1: STATEMENT OF INTENT

I, ... being presently of sound mind, wilfully and voluntarily execute this advance statement to ensure that, during periods of incapacity resulting from psychiatric illness my choices regarding my mental health care will be carried out despite my inability to make informed decisions on my own behalf. I intend this document to take precedence over all other means of ascertaining my intent during periods of such incapacity.

To the extent, if any, that this document would not be considered valid in law it is my desire that it be considered a statement of my wishes and that it be accorded the greatest possible legal weight and respect. I understand that this statement will become active and take effect upon my incapacity.

The fact that there may be some incomplete sections or blanks in this document, should not affect its validity in any way. I intend that all completed sections be followed.

This advance statement is valid from the date on which it is signed unless I decide to renew or dispose of it.

SIGNED

Date

I confirm that this form has been completed by the above named person

Witness 1   Name   _____

             Address   _____

                         _____

             Postcode   _____

             Signed   _____   Date _____

Witness 2   Name   _____

             Address   _____

                         _____

             Postcode   _____

             Signed   _____   Date _____

My Advance Directives are as follows:

If I am experiencing mental health difficulties **I do not want** the following to happen:

I do not wish to take the following medication:

My wishes are as follows:

I have found the following medication helpful:

If I am experiencing mental health difficulties I would like the following to happen:

In the past I have found the following helpful:

If I decide to stay at home I want the following to happen:

My wishes continued:

If I go into hospital I would like the following to happen:

I would like the following to happen regarding my home:

My finances

I would like my finances to be handled by:

I would trust this person to handle the following (delete as appropriate)

- look after credit cards and bank book
- cash benefits
- pay bills
- any other expenses

I do not want my finances handled by:

Other information I agree to share as necessary

NHS Number:

My Date of Birth:

My Current Address:

THE FOLLOWING NAMED PEOPLE, WHERE POSSIBLE, AGREE TO CARRY OUT MY WISHES AS STATED ABOVE

I agree to the following contact details being shared as needed

Care Coordinator:

Next of Kin:

Solicitor:

Advocate:

Social Worker:

Community Psychiatric Nurse:

General Practitioner:

Day Centre Key worker

Relatives to be informed:

Relatives not to be informed:

Friends to be informed:

Other people not to be informed:

I agree to the following people having a copy of my advance statement

Name   Name

Address   Address

Other Publications by the authors of this workbook

Wonderfully Strange

By

Becky Shaw

This book will help if you; have ever been 'labelled', worried about using mental health services, wondered how you'd cope if someone you know has mental health problems or you simply need to understand the system.

After years of feeling an outsider, Becky is now an established author with contributions to academic journals and books. Her experience has given her a passion to help others who've had problems in dealing with mental health issues. This book is an account of her journey through the system, plus practical help on how to manage, where to go and how to survive.

Becky says, "A nurse described me as 'Wonderfully Strange.' I don't know if it was intended as a compliment. It is a description of me that fits. I have a different outlook on life: but I am wonderful and I am loved."

Stop Paddling / Start Sailing

By

Roger Smith

Parts of Roger's life in and out of psychiatric wards are told as a short fantasy then expanded to reveal experiences, events and interactions. He uses the analogy of a river journey to describe events and what it is like to be diagnosed as having bipolar disorder.

This is the first book to discuss knowledge of memes and memetics as part of the management of mental health. These ideas can allow readers to see the world in a very different way.

Discovering Recovery

By the

Rushcliffe Mental Heath Support Group

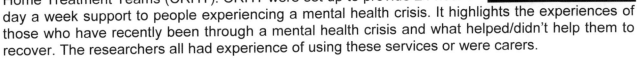

The Rushcliffe Mental Health Support Group provides peer support for people who have difficulties with their mental health and their carers. Members of the group are in different stages of recovery creating a forum for sharing experiences of mental health distress and support and ideas from others on how to cope. The group offers social activities, information signposting, delivers training/workshops and conducts research. Through this book we wanted to share the effect that the experience of a small support group can have on individuals, to share our experiences of what helps, what does not help when experiencing mental distress and to tell you about our individual experiences of mental health services. The book highlights *the recovery process* from mental distress. It offers hope and optimism for those currently in distress, and tips for supporters.

Reality of Crisis

By Amaze

(Becky Shaw and Val Stapleton)

This report is about the outcomes of research into the experience of having a mental health crisis and accessing the Crisis Resolution and Home Treatment Teams (CRHT). CRHT were set up to provide 24 hour 7 day a week support to people experiencing a mental health crisis. It highlights the experiences of those who have recently been through a mental health crisis and what helped/didn't help them to recover. The researchers all had experience of using these services or were carers.

This report highlights:
- ✓ the elements of the crisis support which are working,
- ✓ those which are not,
- ✓ what support people want in a crisis
- ✓ what helped them towards their recovery

These are inspiring, thought provoking and intriguing stories from acute crisis. A useful easy to digest report for healthcare staff, managers, commissioners, trainers, people who have used the services, friends and family.

Further copies of this workbook

The books featured on pages 108 and 109 as well as further copies of this workbook are available from www.rsgbooks.co.uk where discounts can be requested for bulk purchases.

Advance Statements training can be tailored to your needs. Details of Advance Statements training and a range of other workshops and courses can be found at www.mentalation.co.uk / www.stoppaddling.co.uk

All of the information in this workbook is given in good faith but legally may not be precise interpretations of the law. These definitions and notes are given so that you may find out more detail if you wish to.

-- -- -- -- --